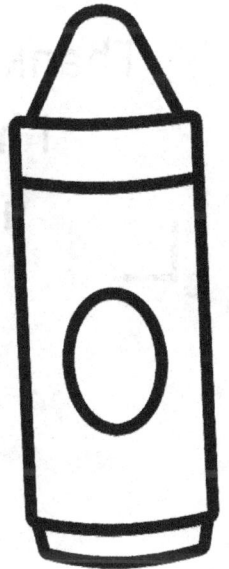

THIS BOOK BELONGS TO:

....

Thank you!

Thank you so much for purchasing this coloring book! I hope you absolutely loved it! Be sur to follow us on Amazon to get updates on new books!

★★★★★

Abella Publishing

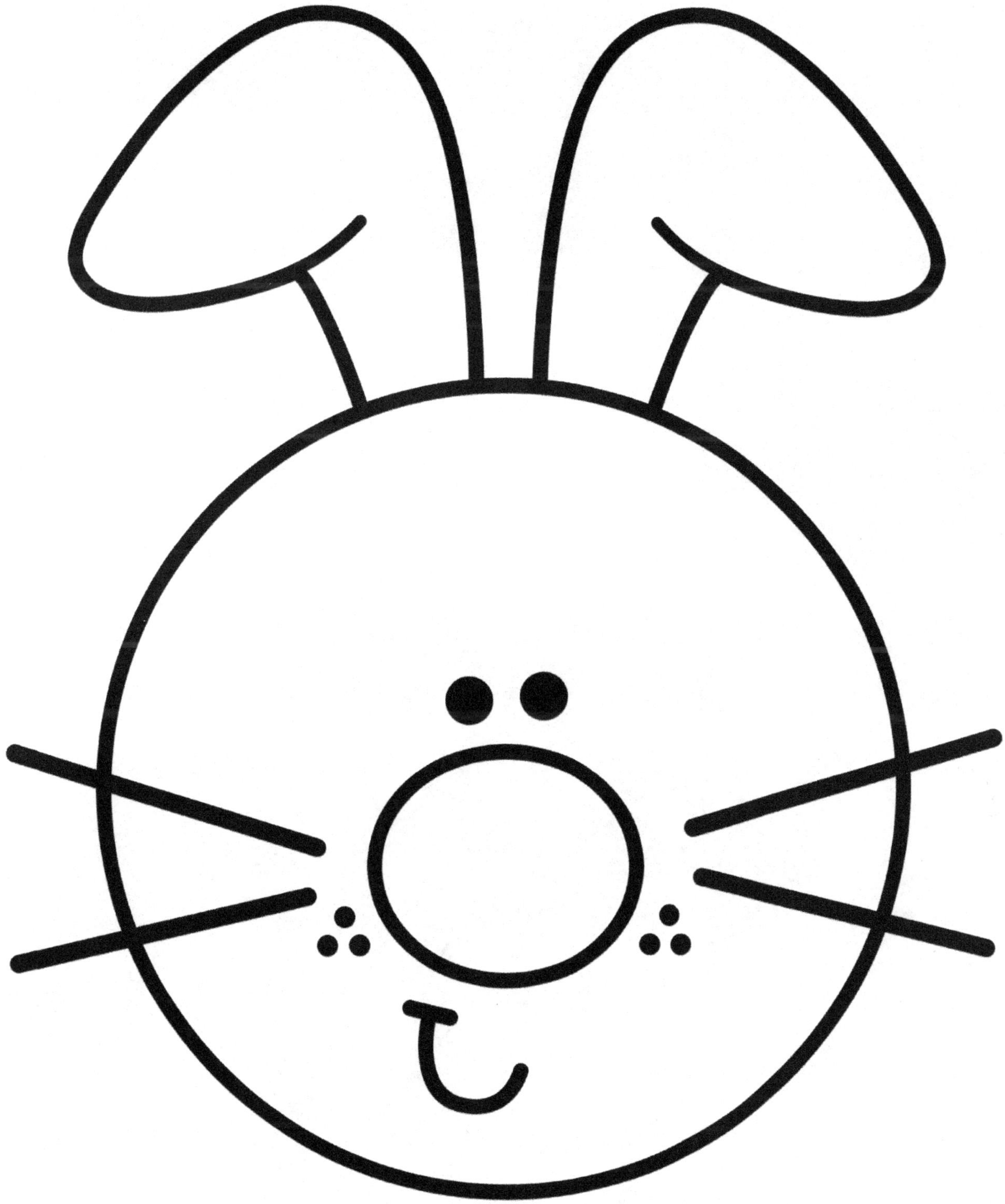

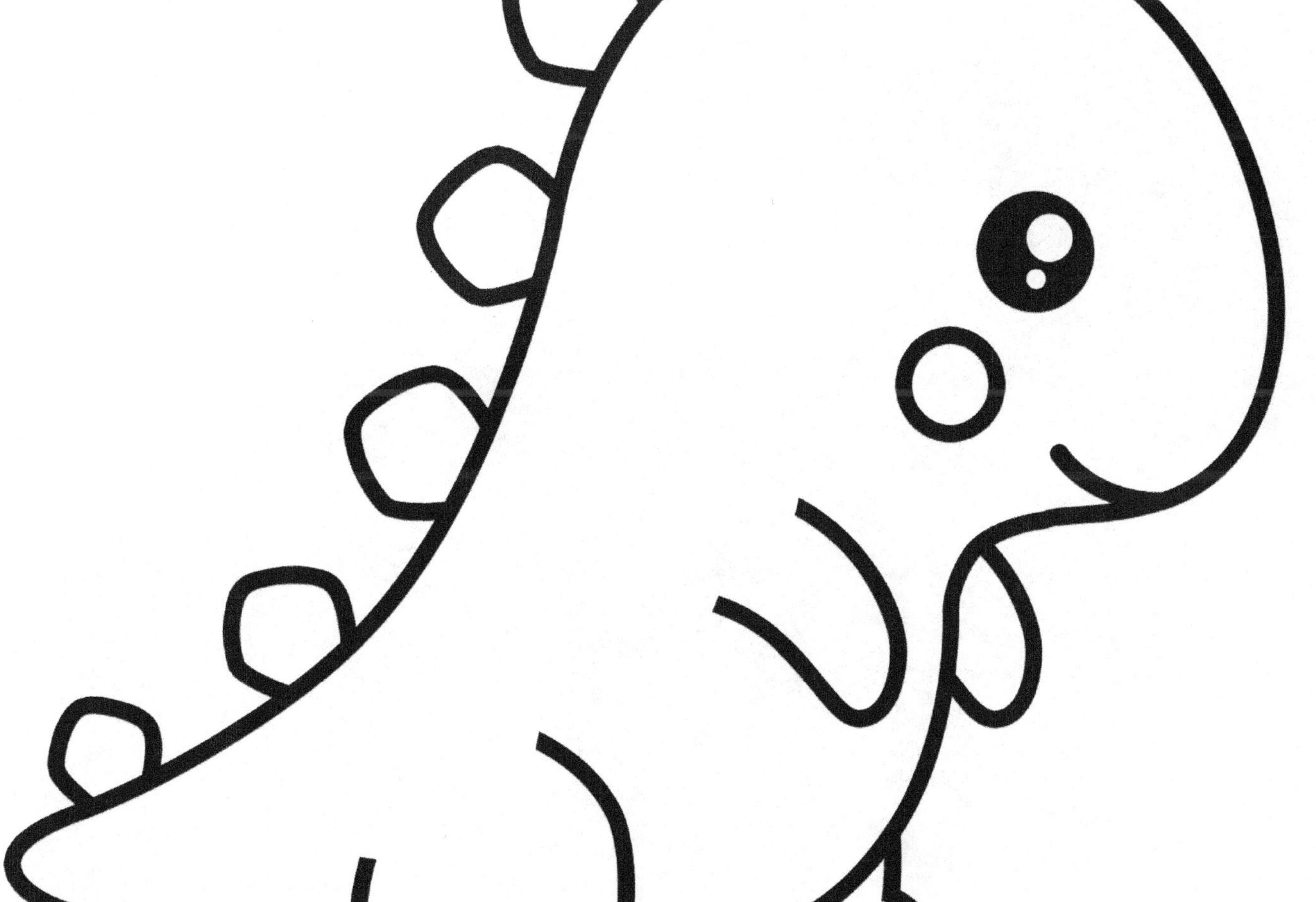

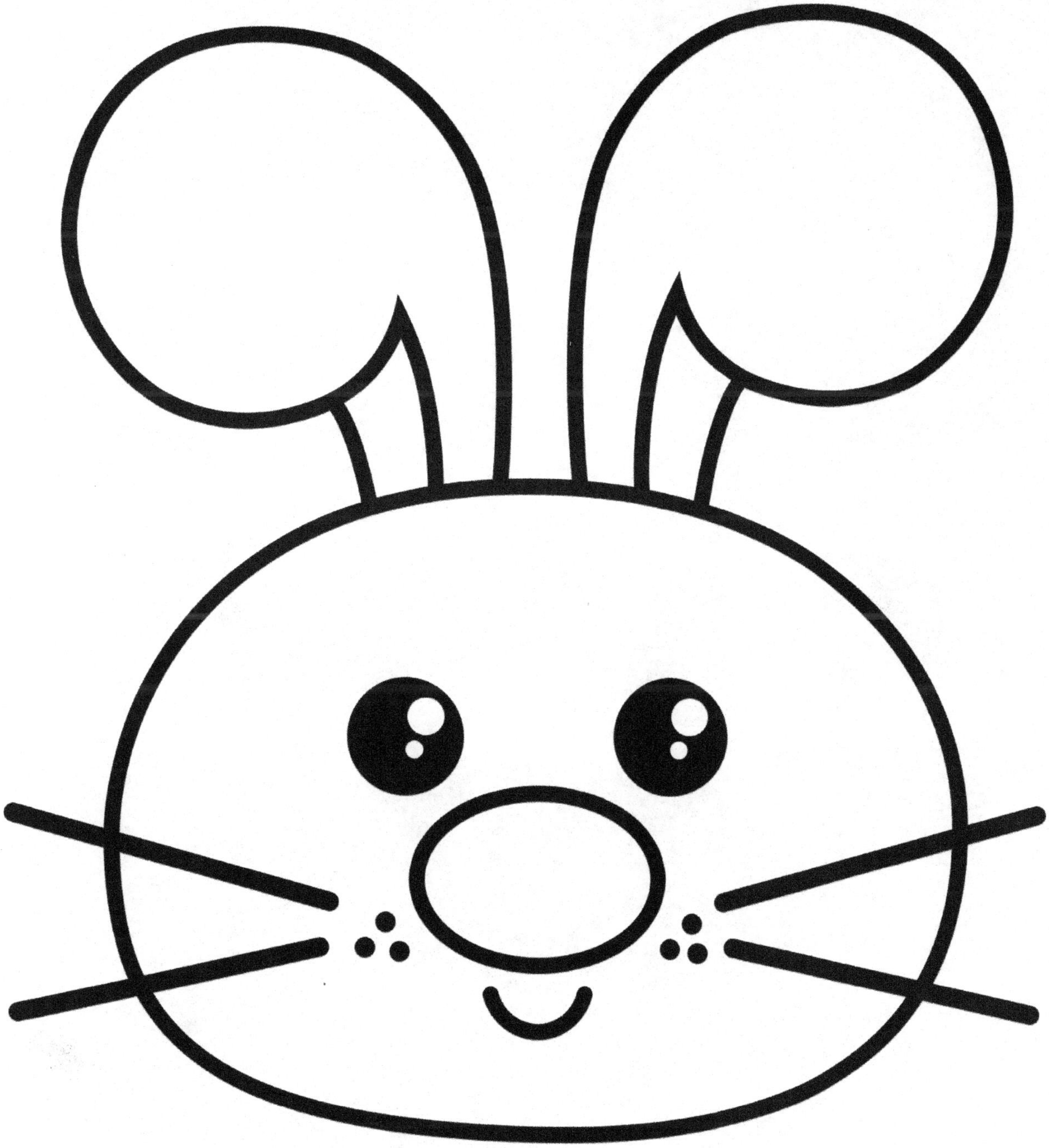

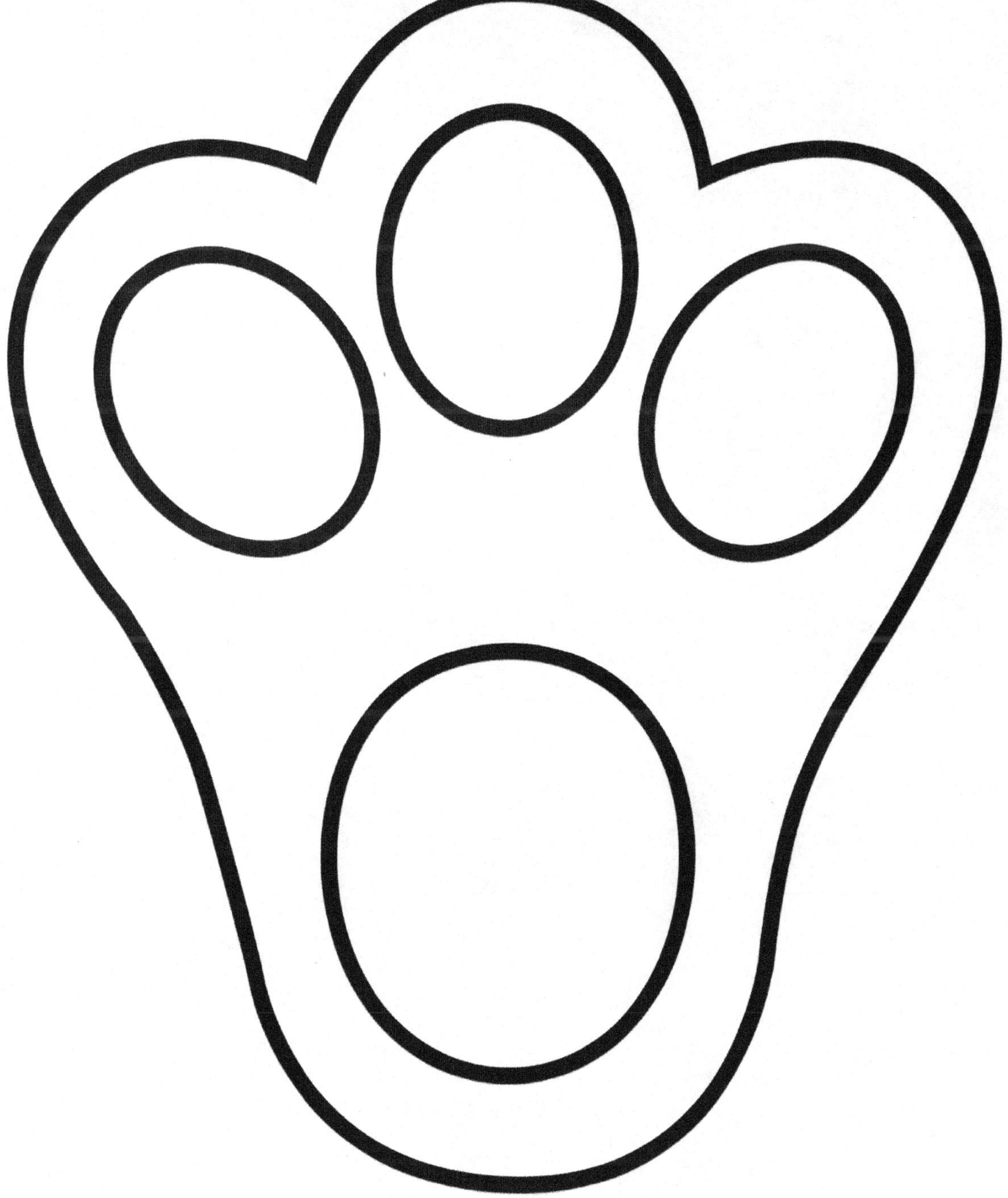

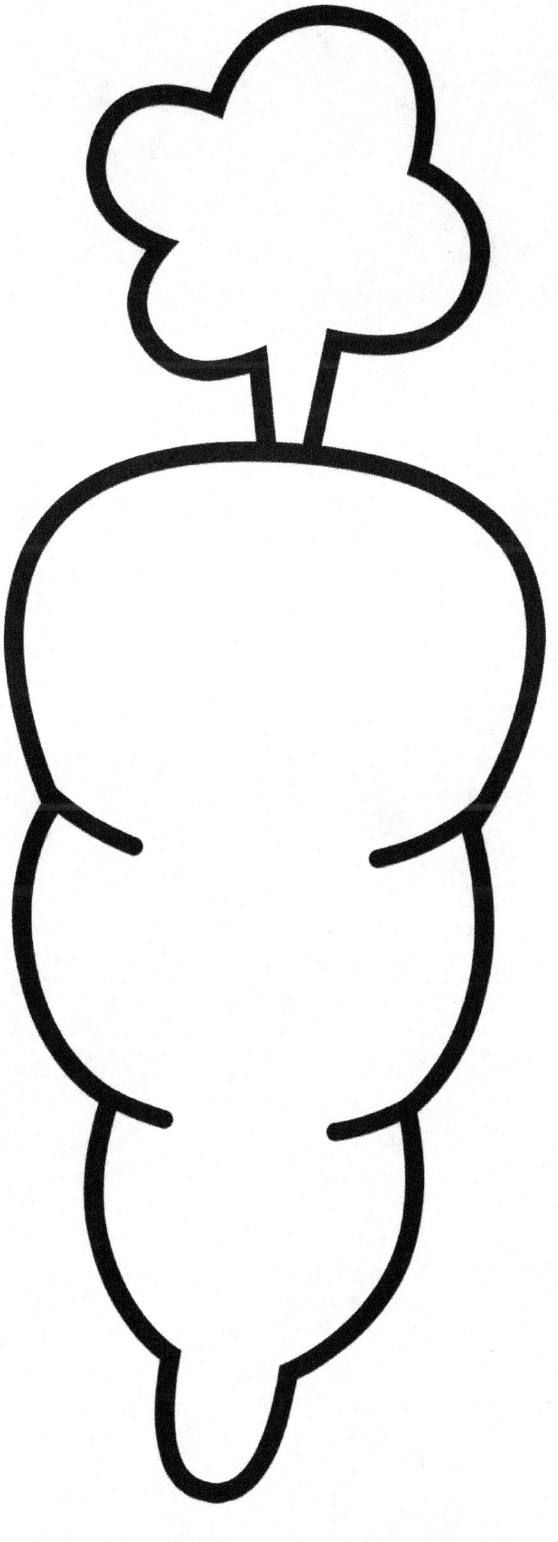

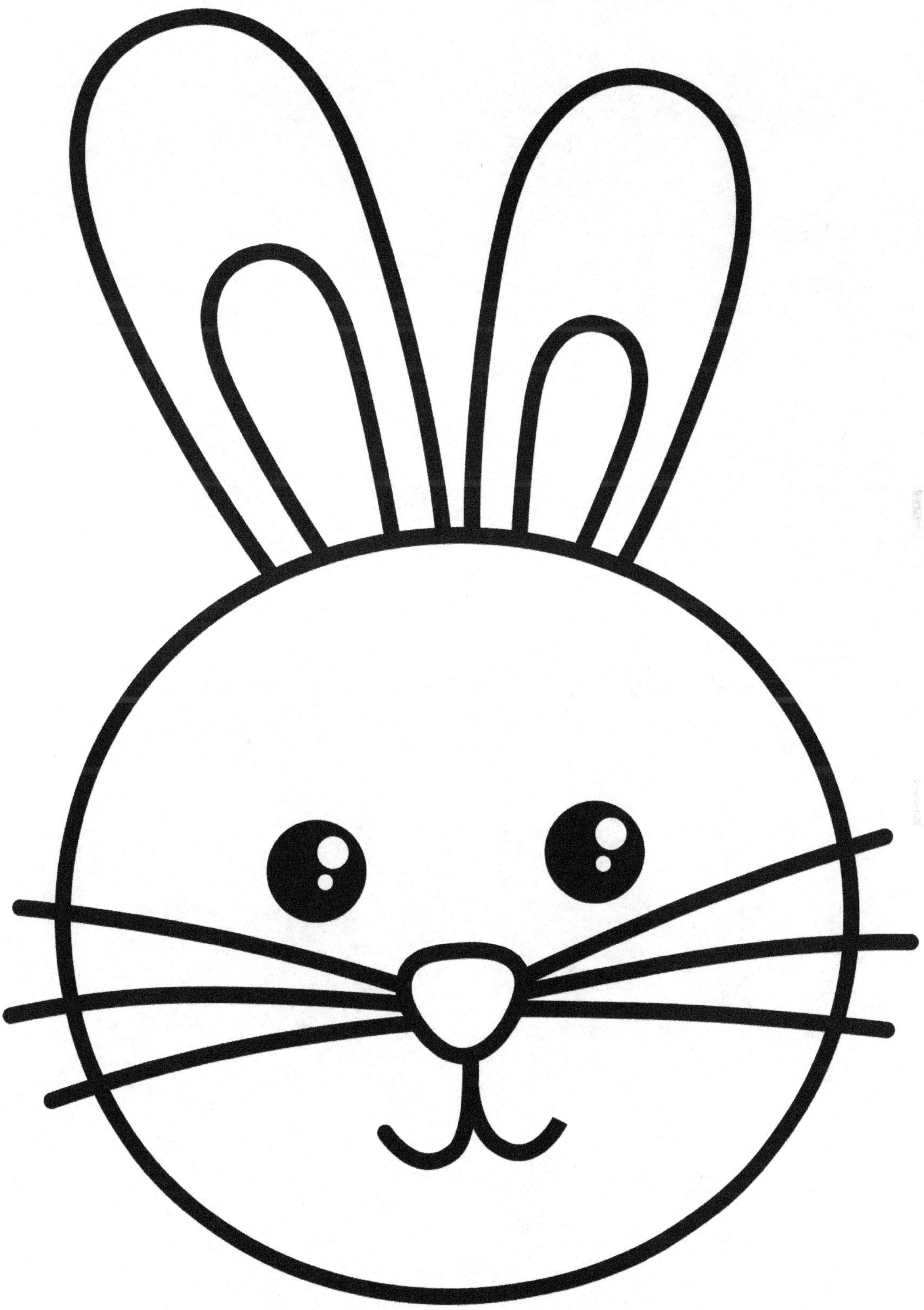

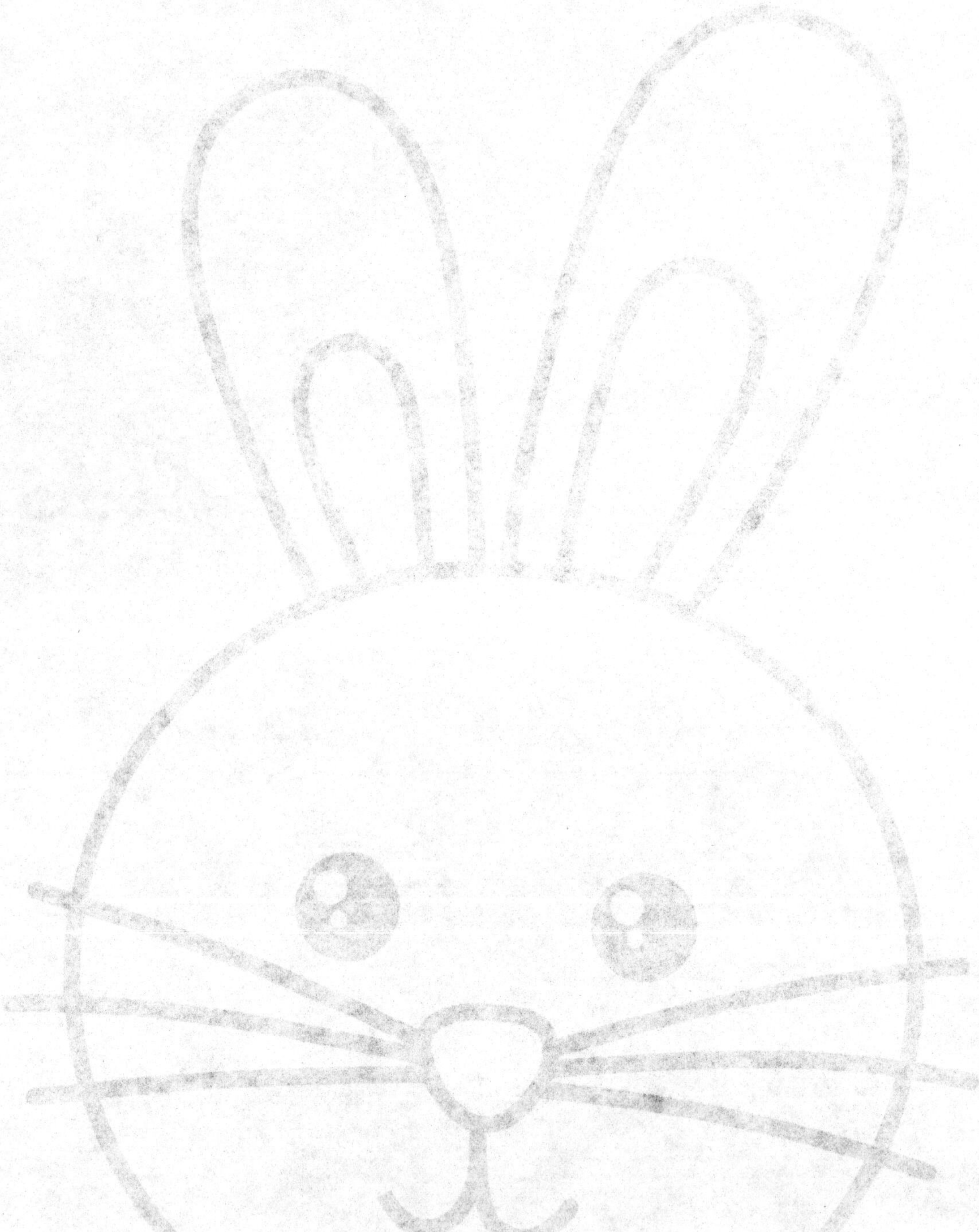

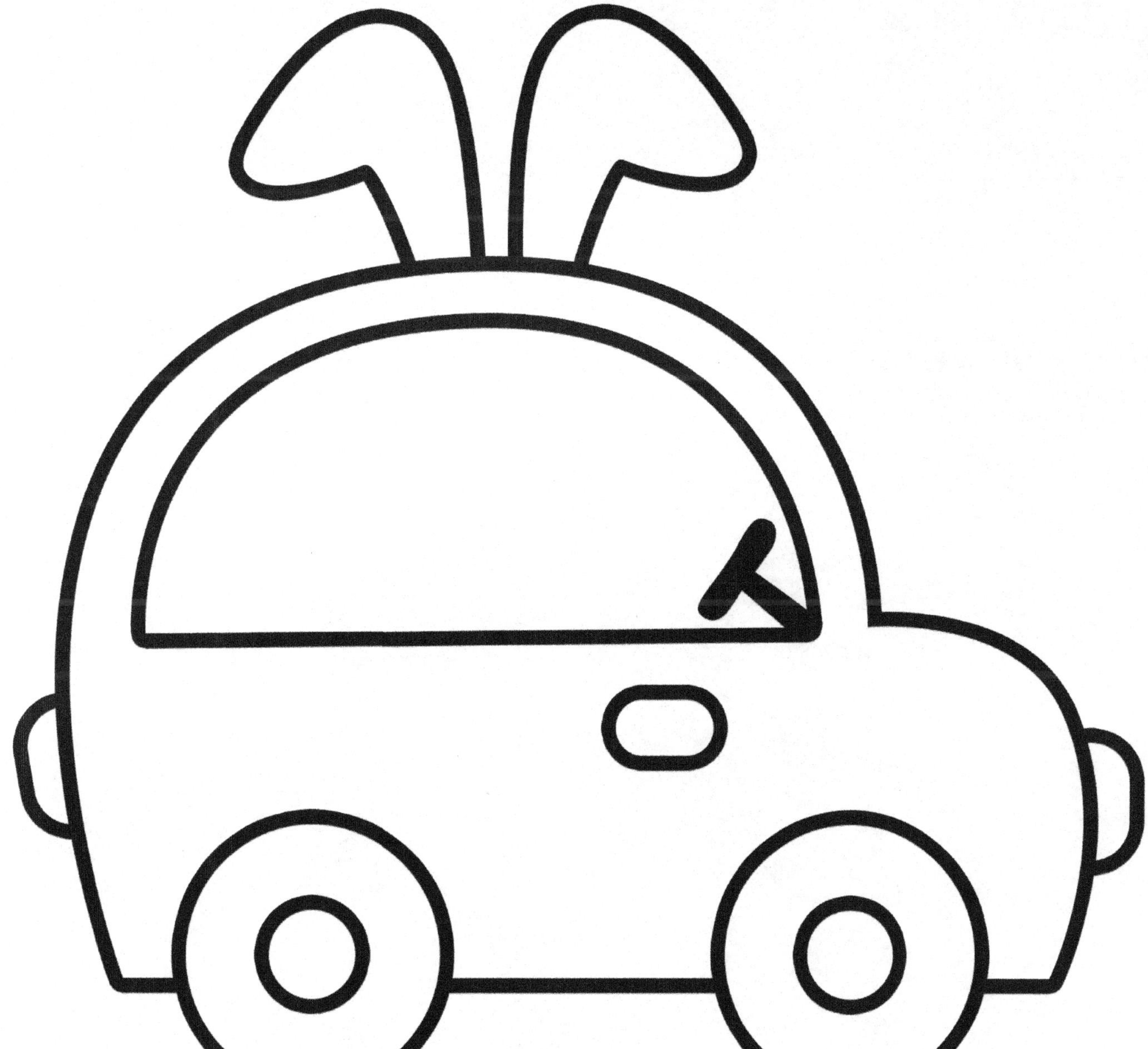

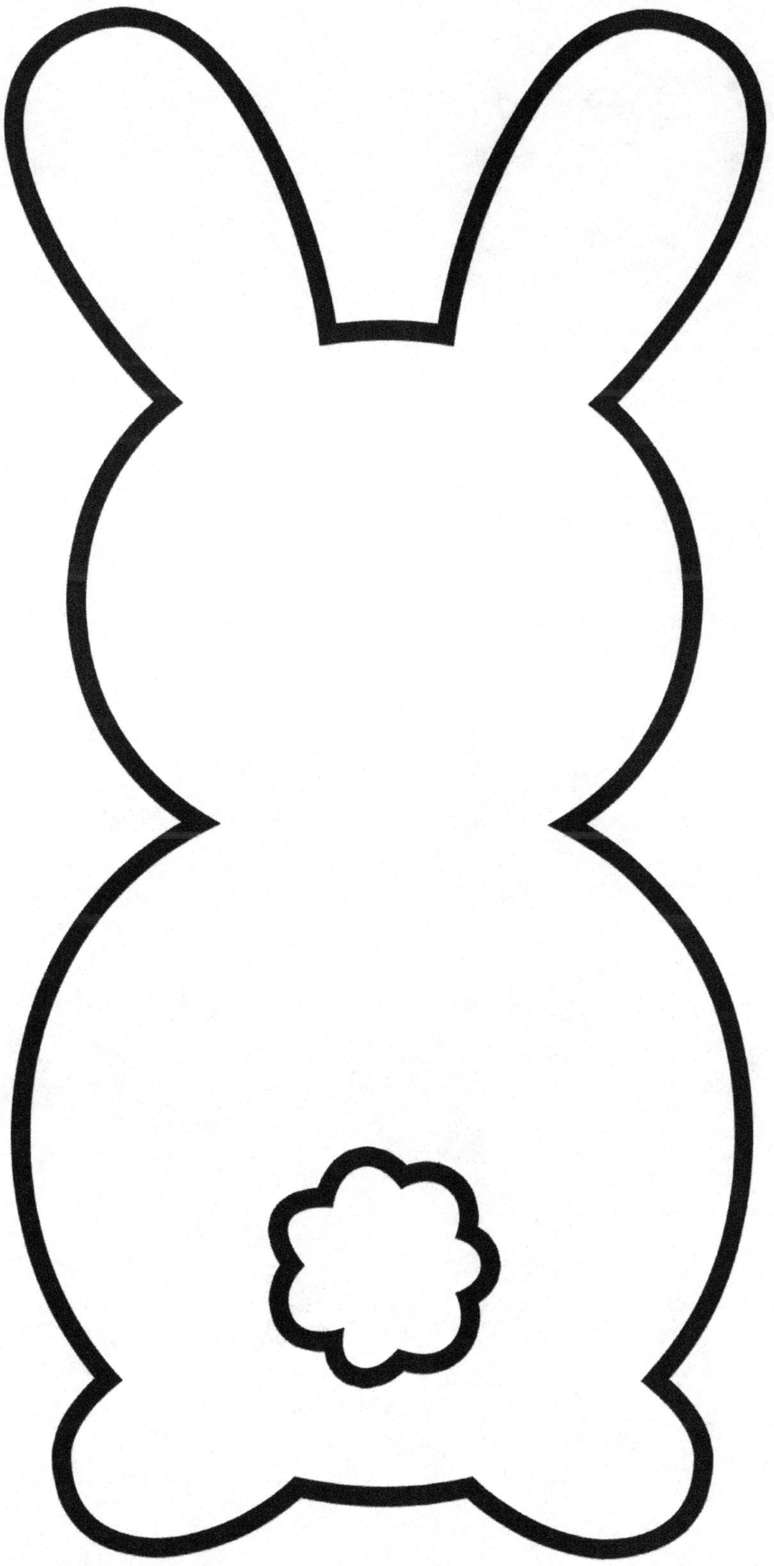

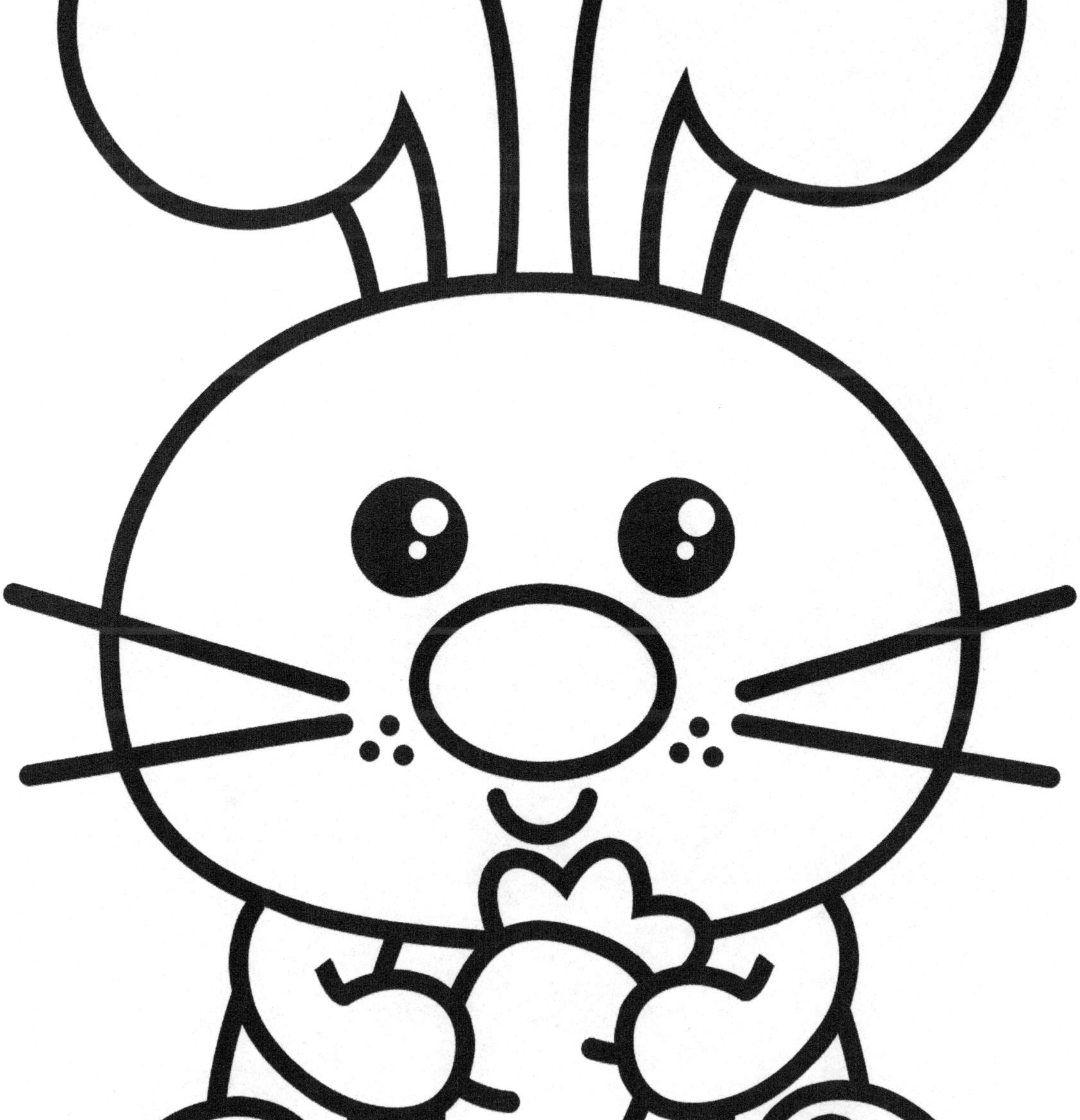

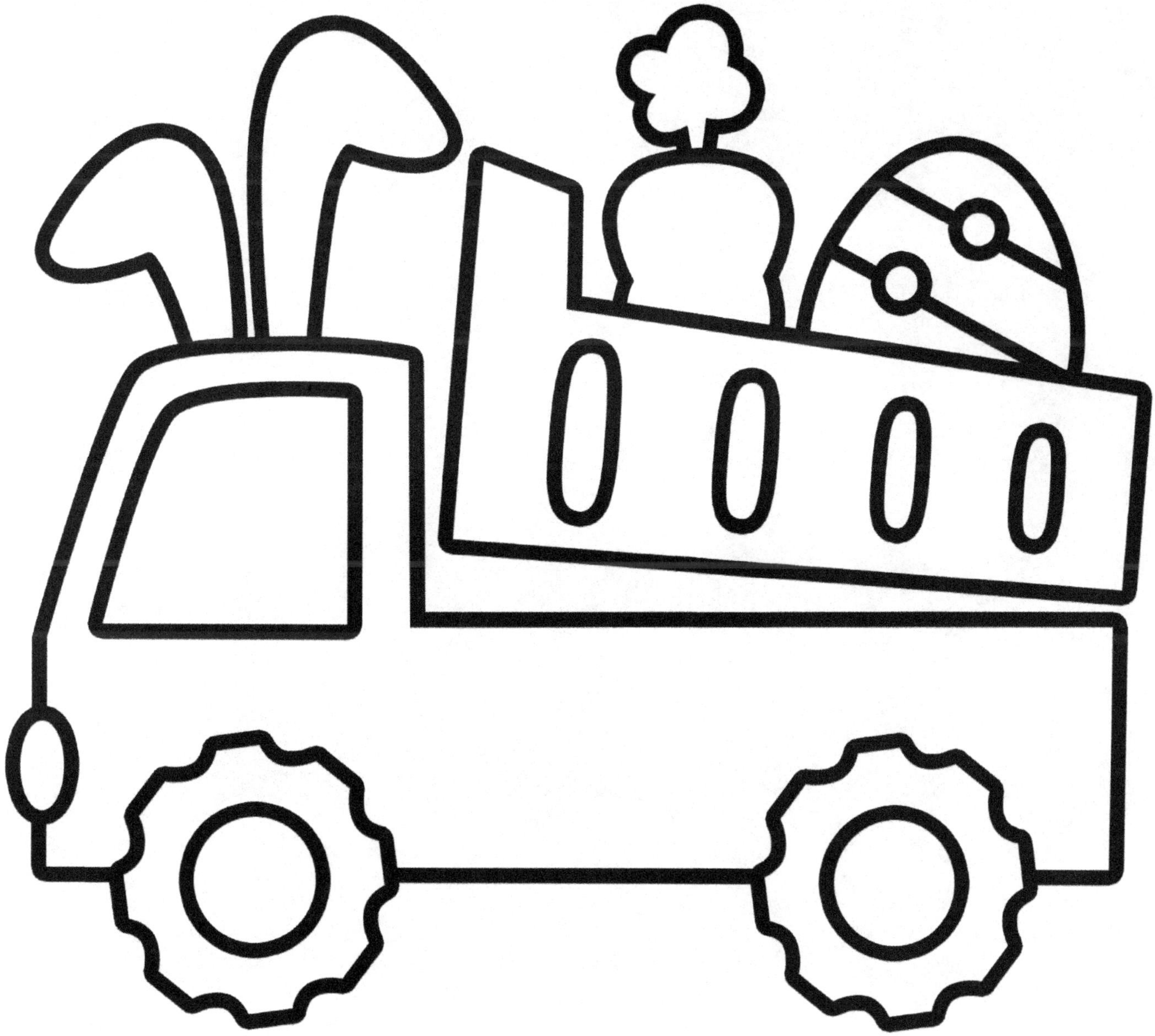

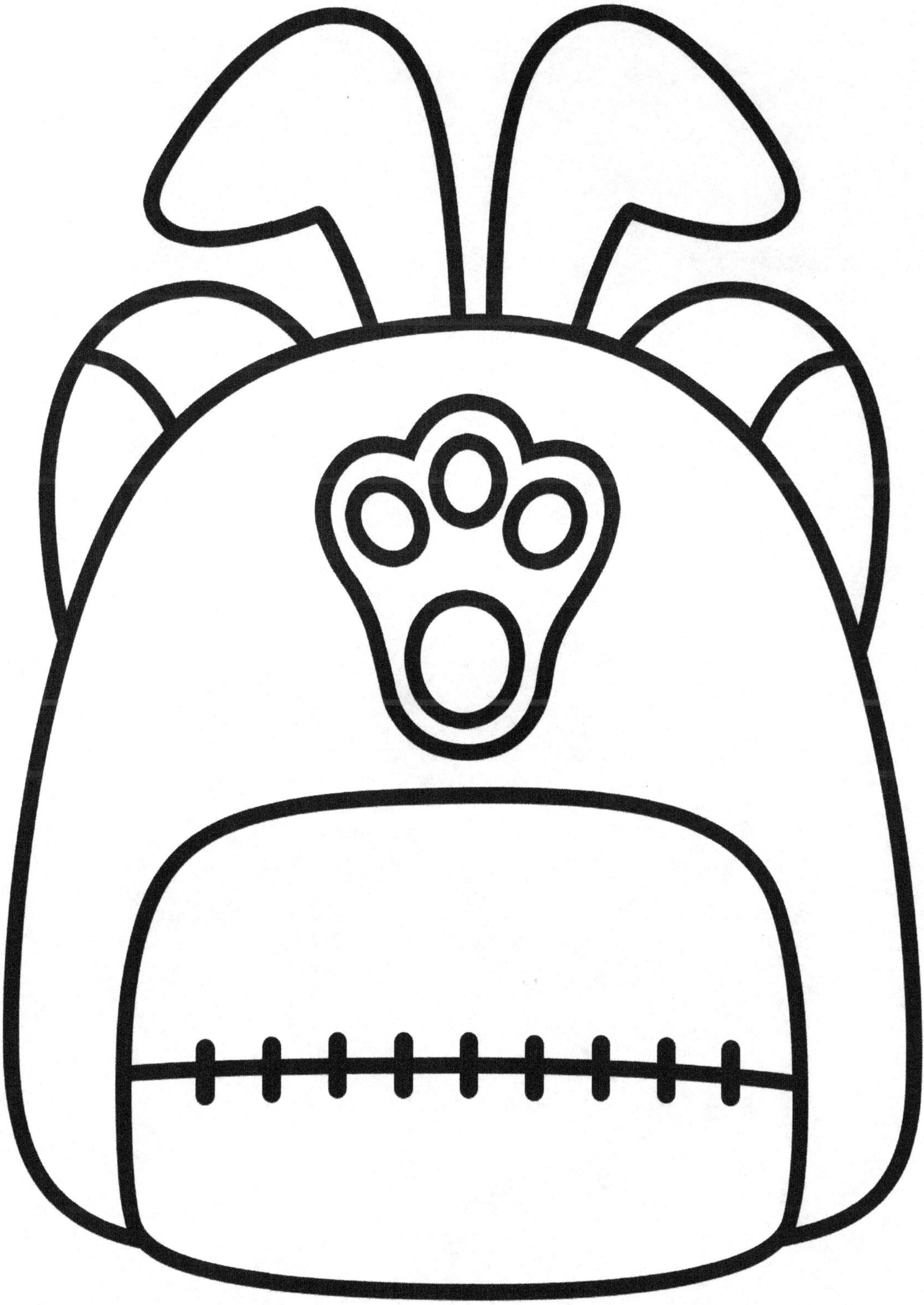

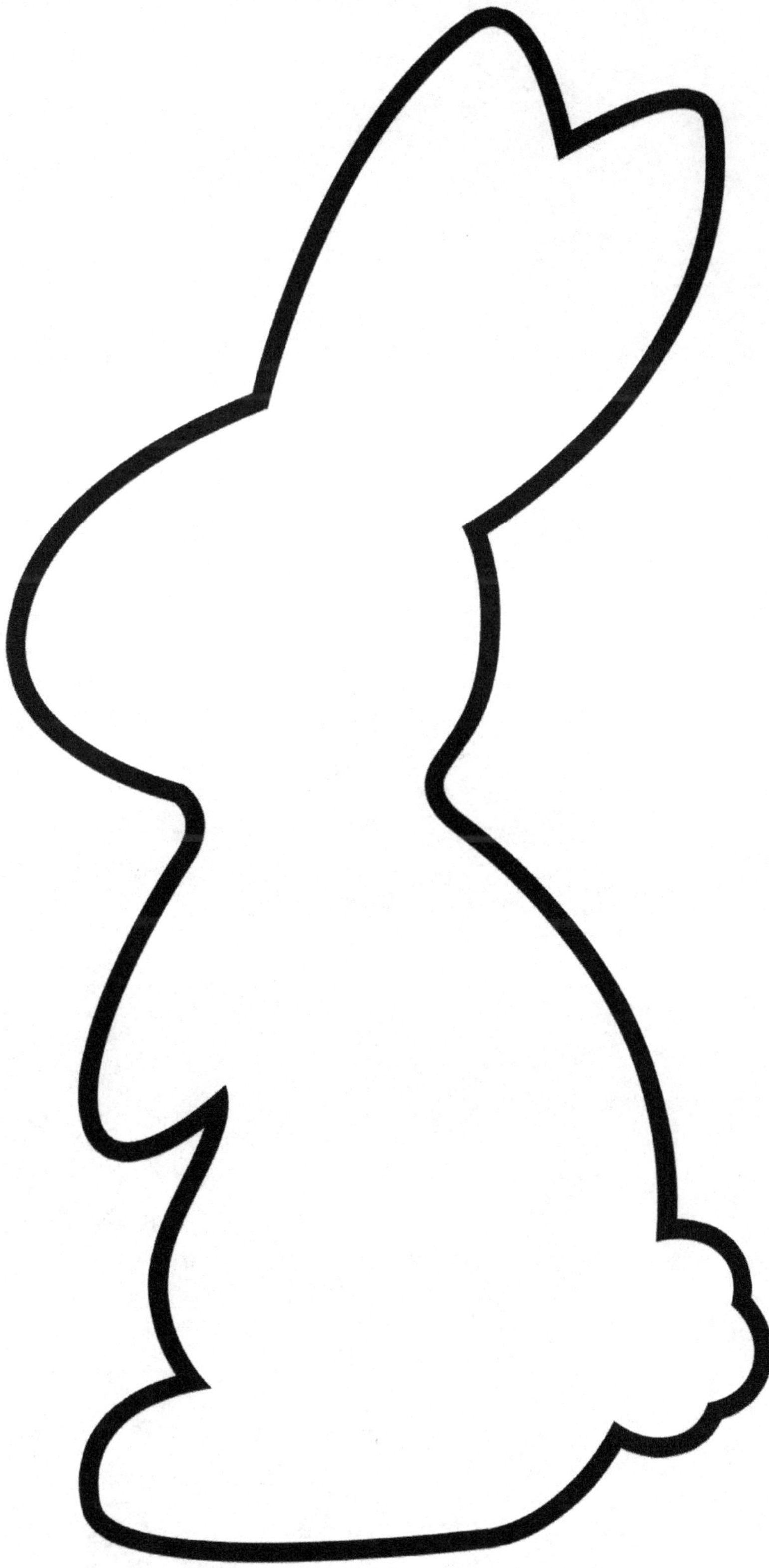

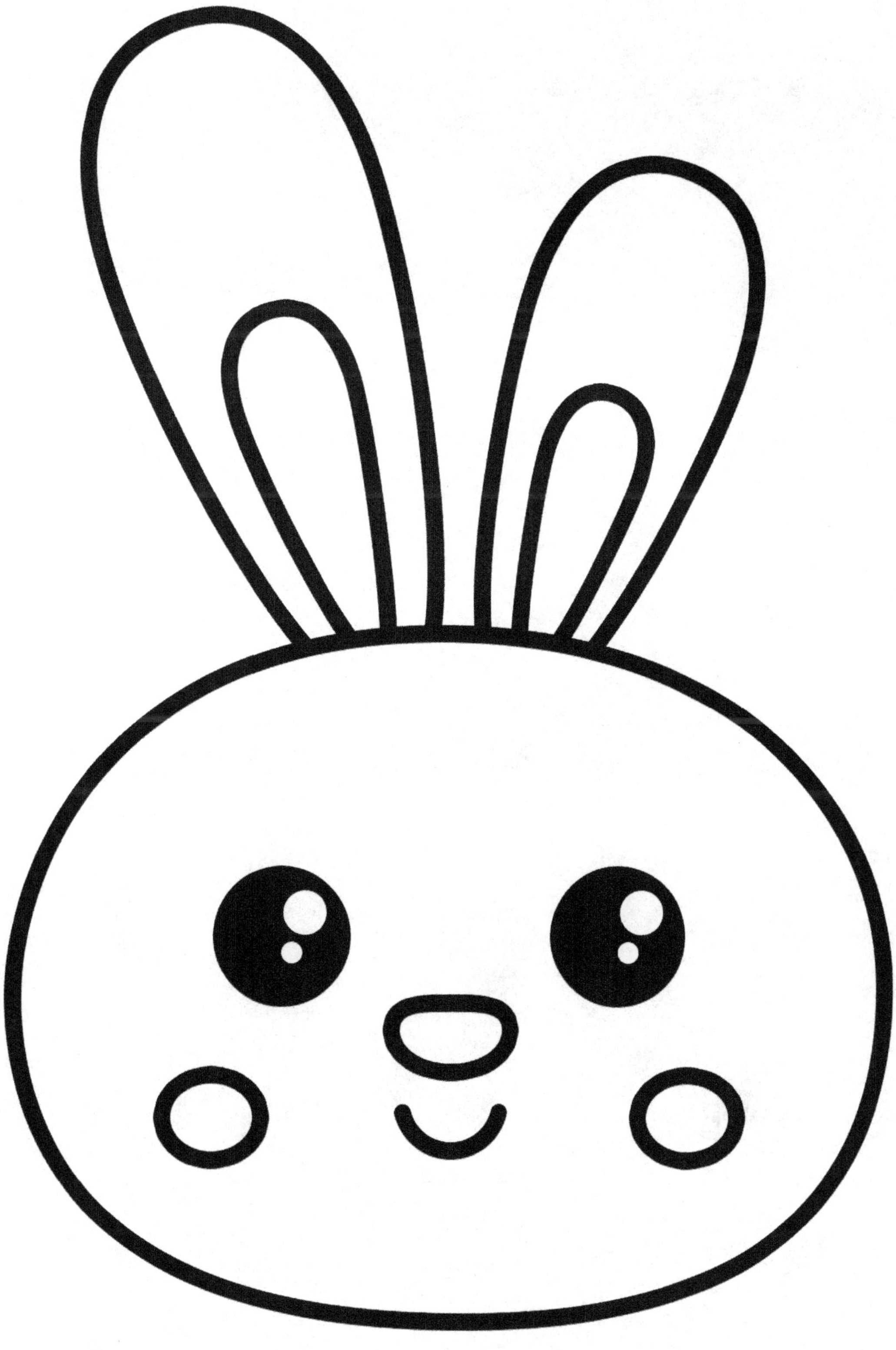

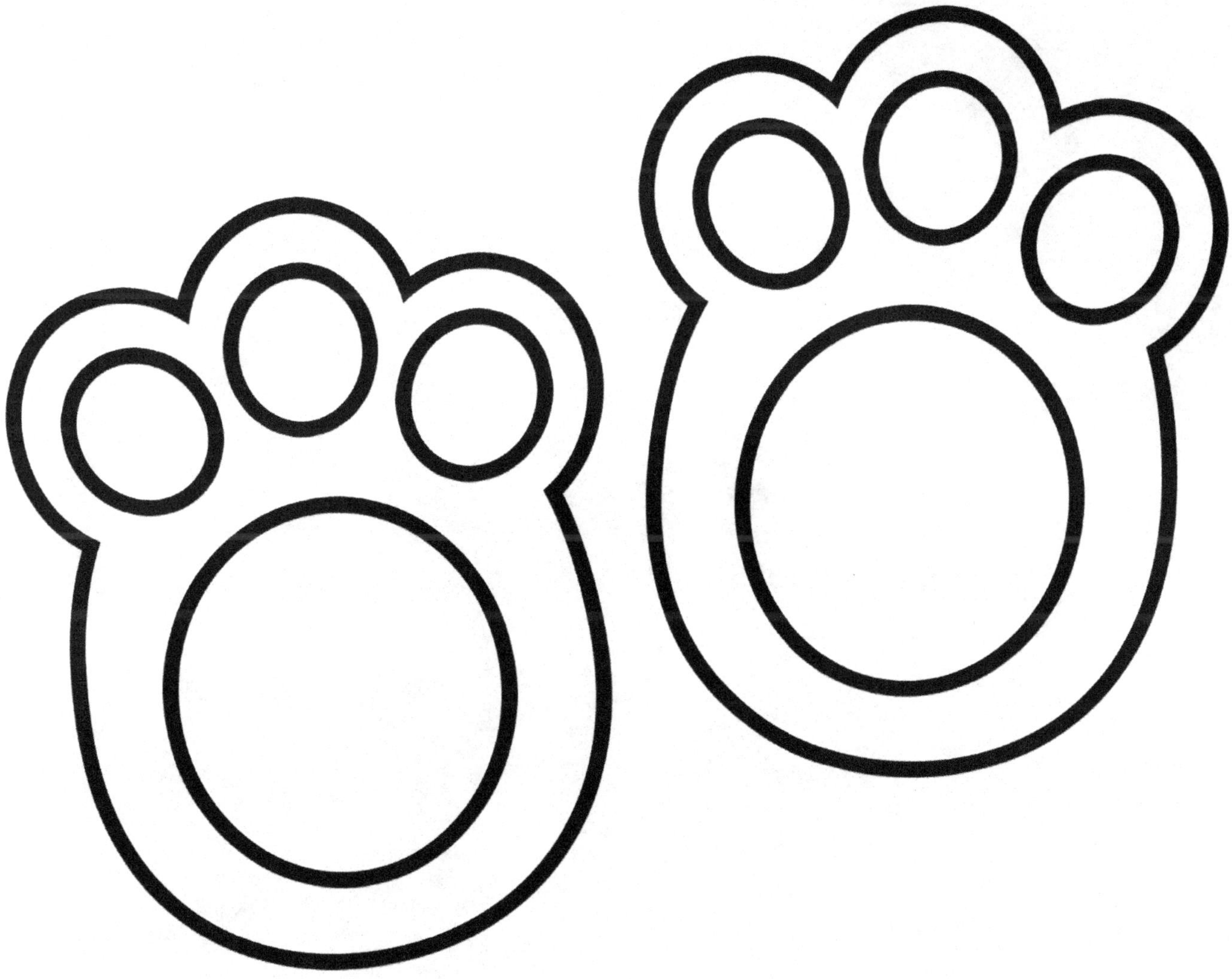

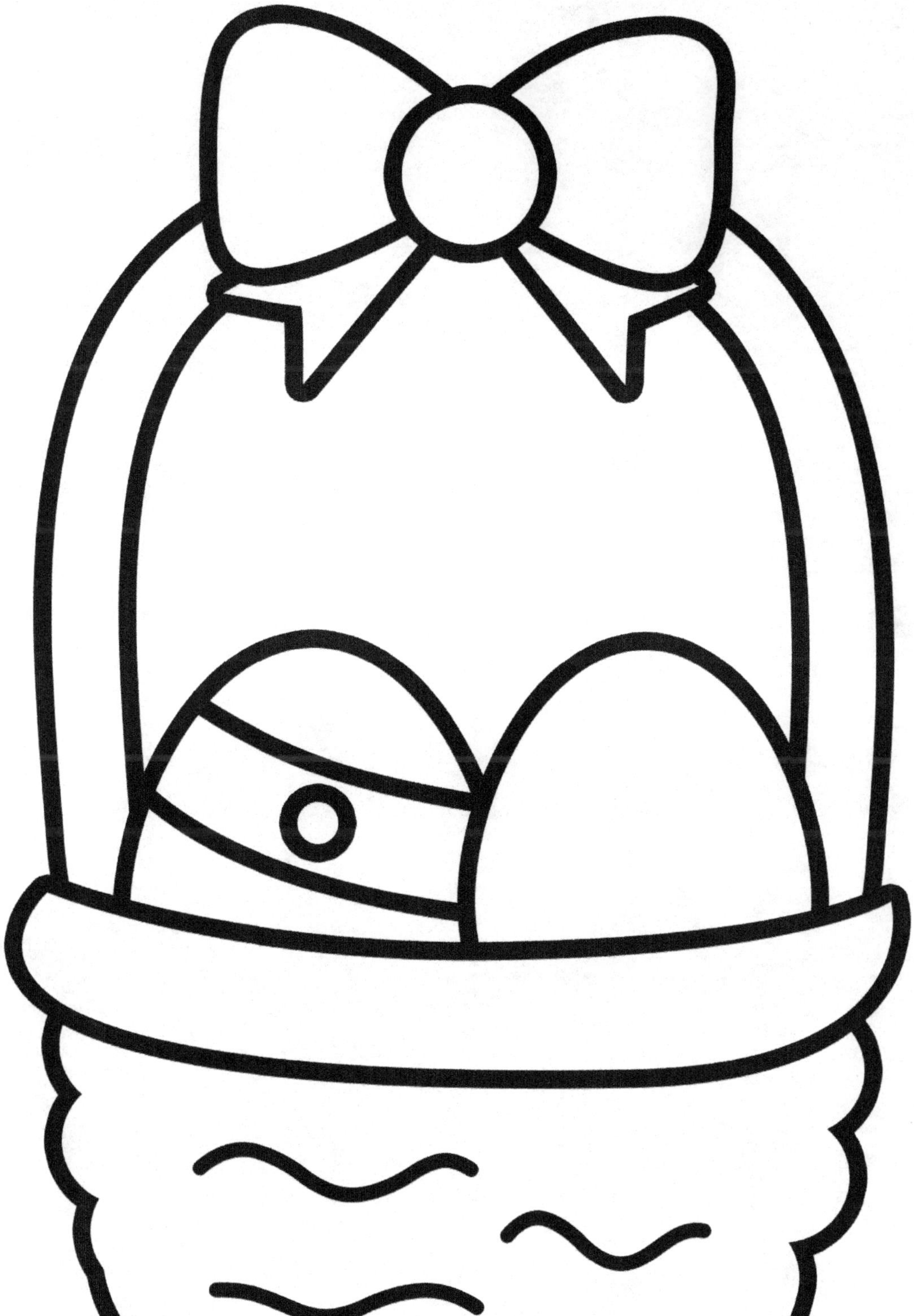

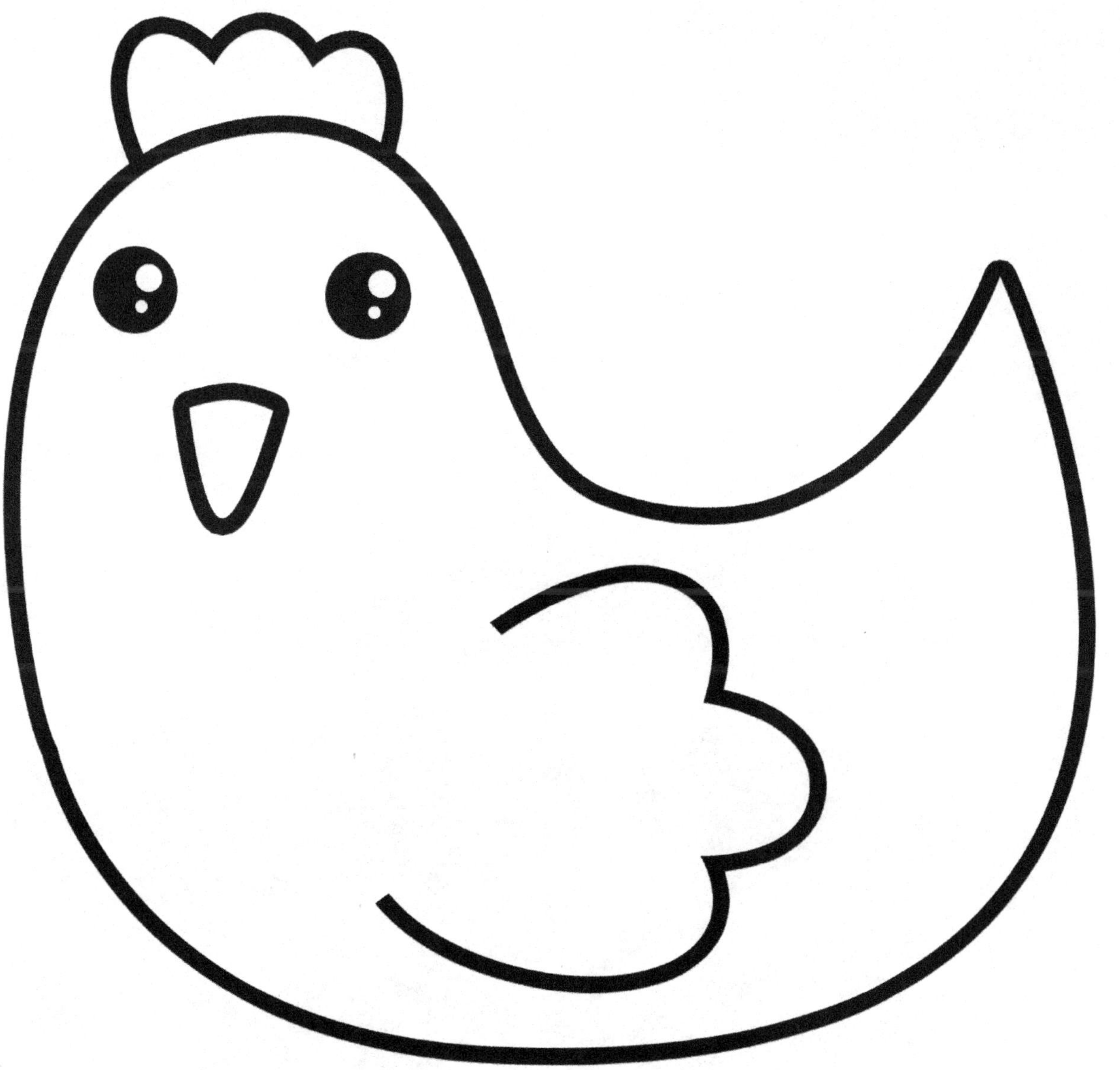

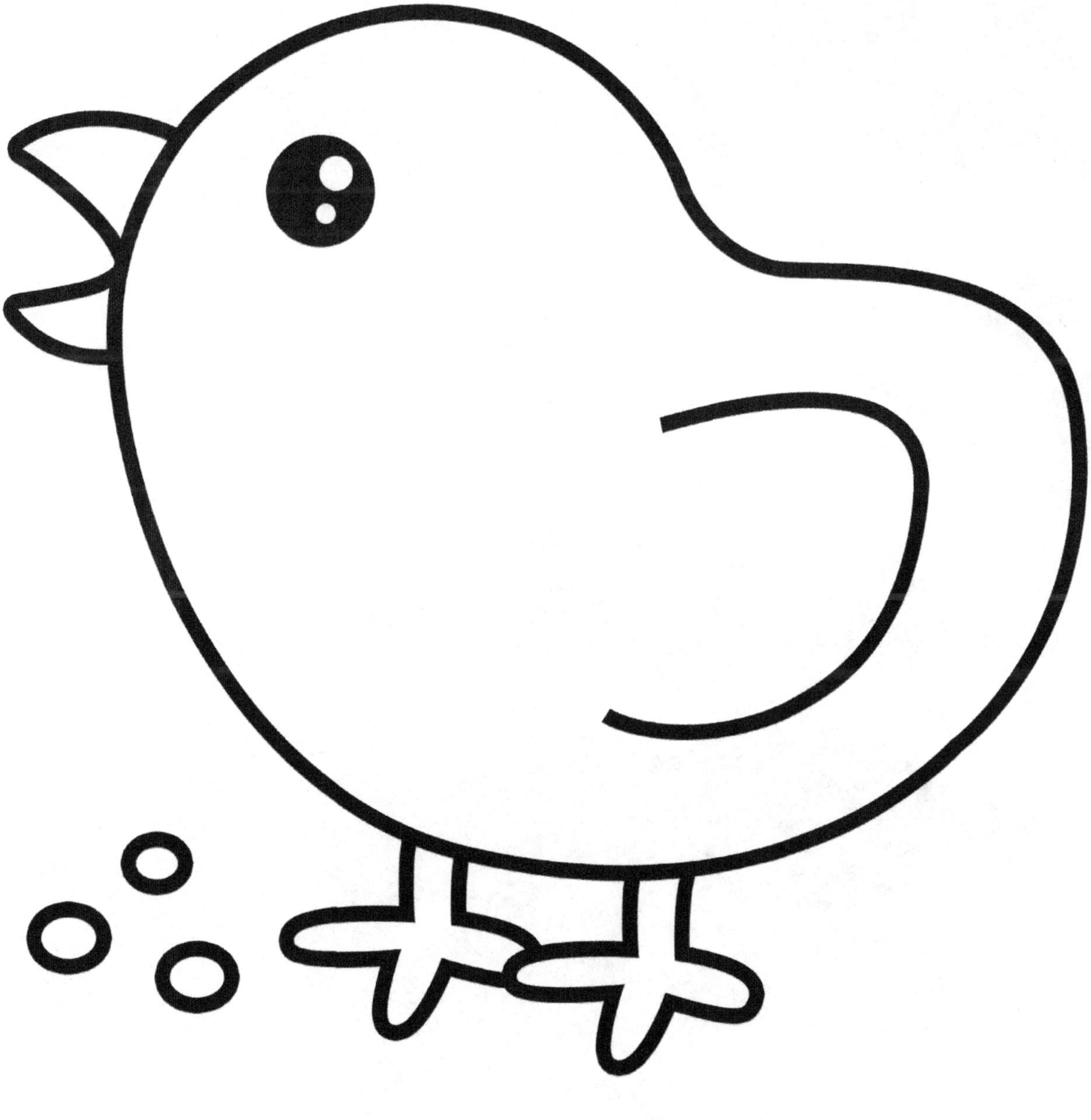

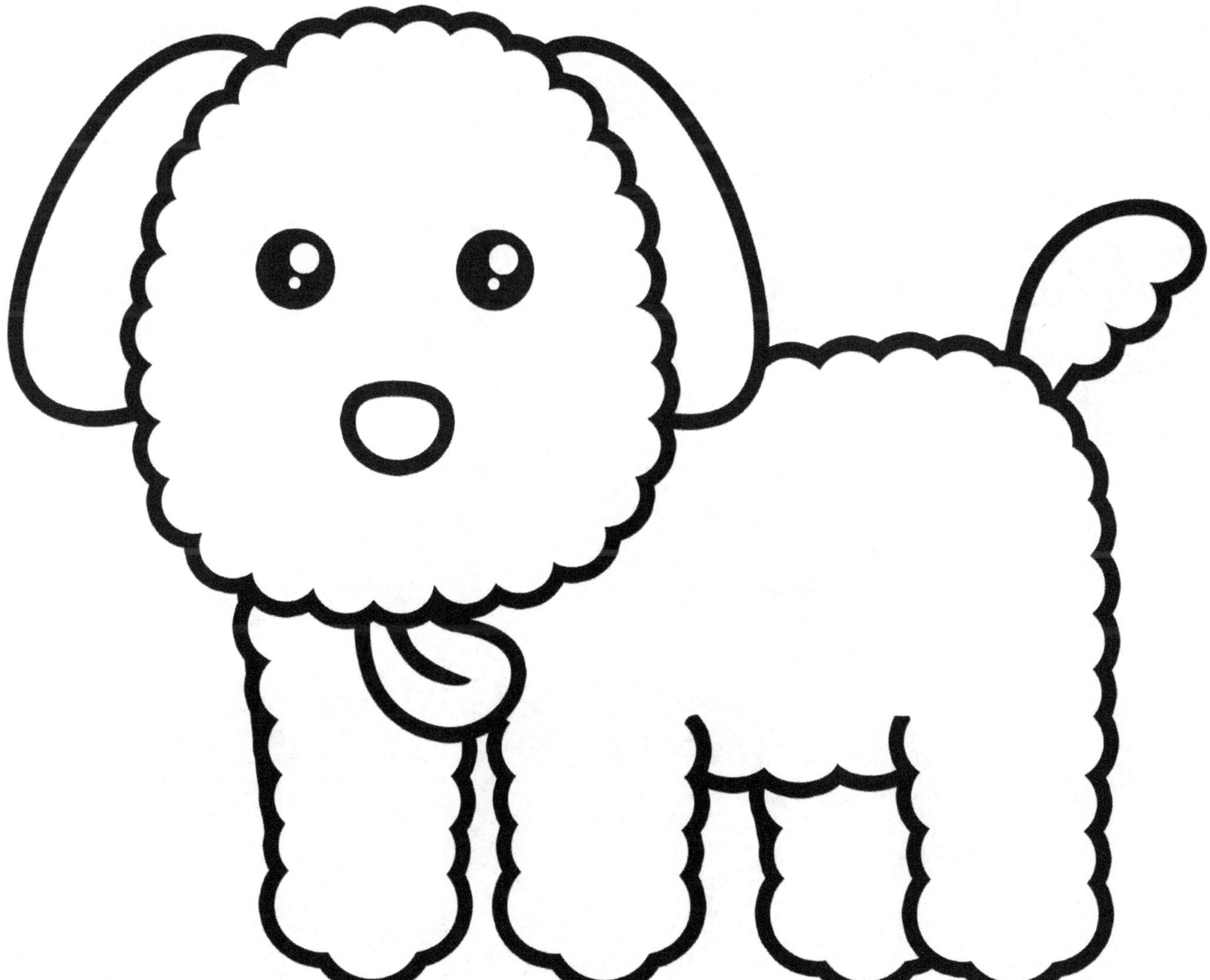

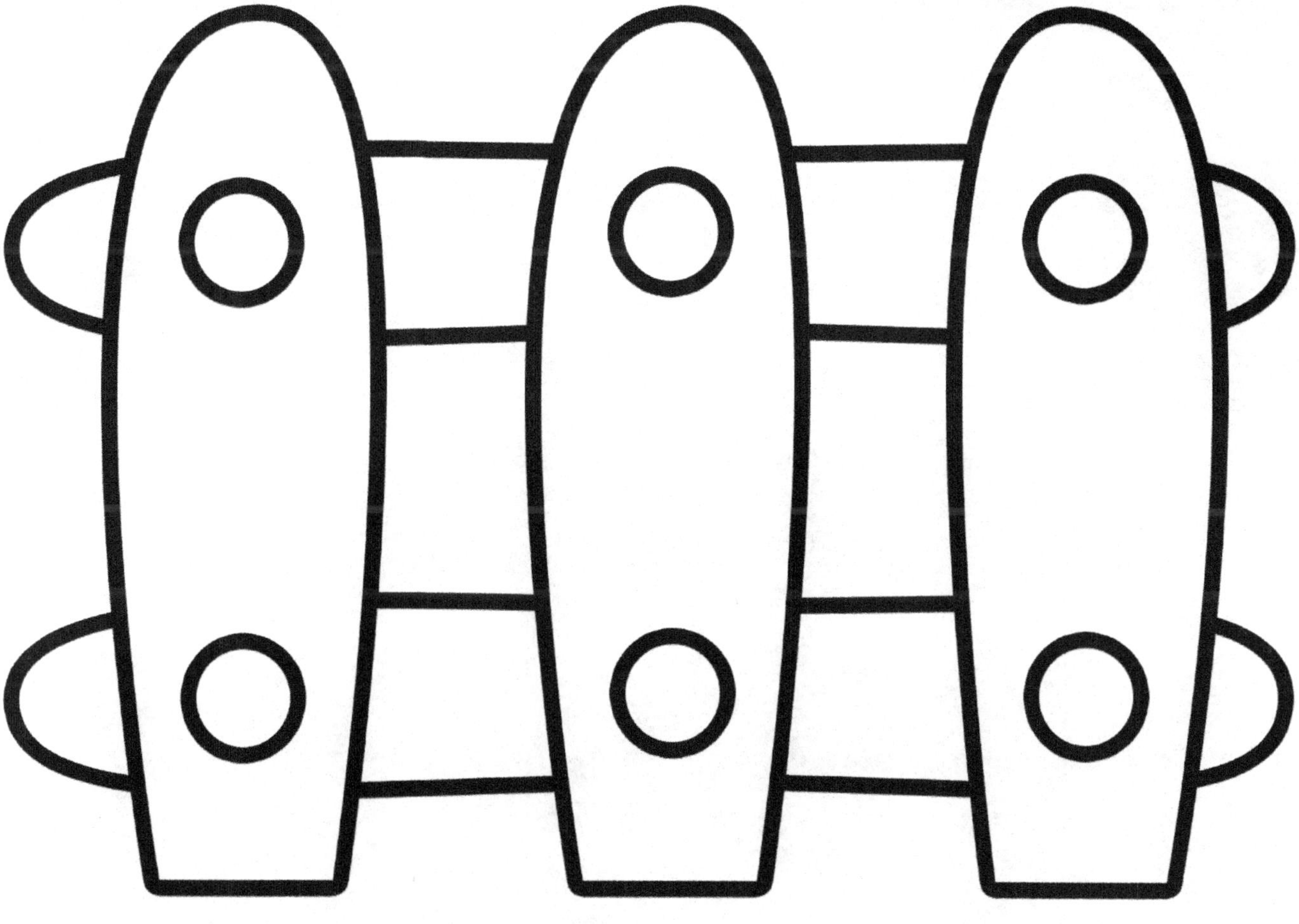

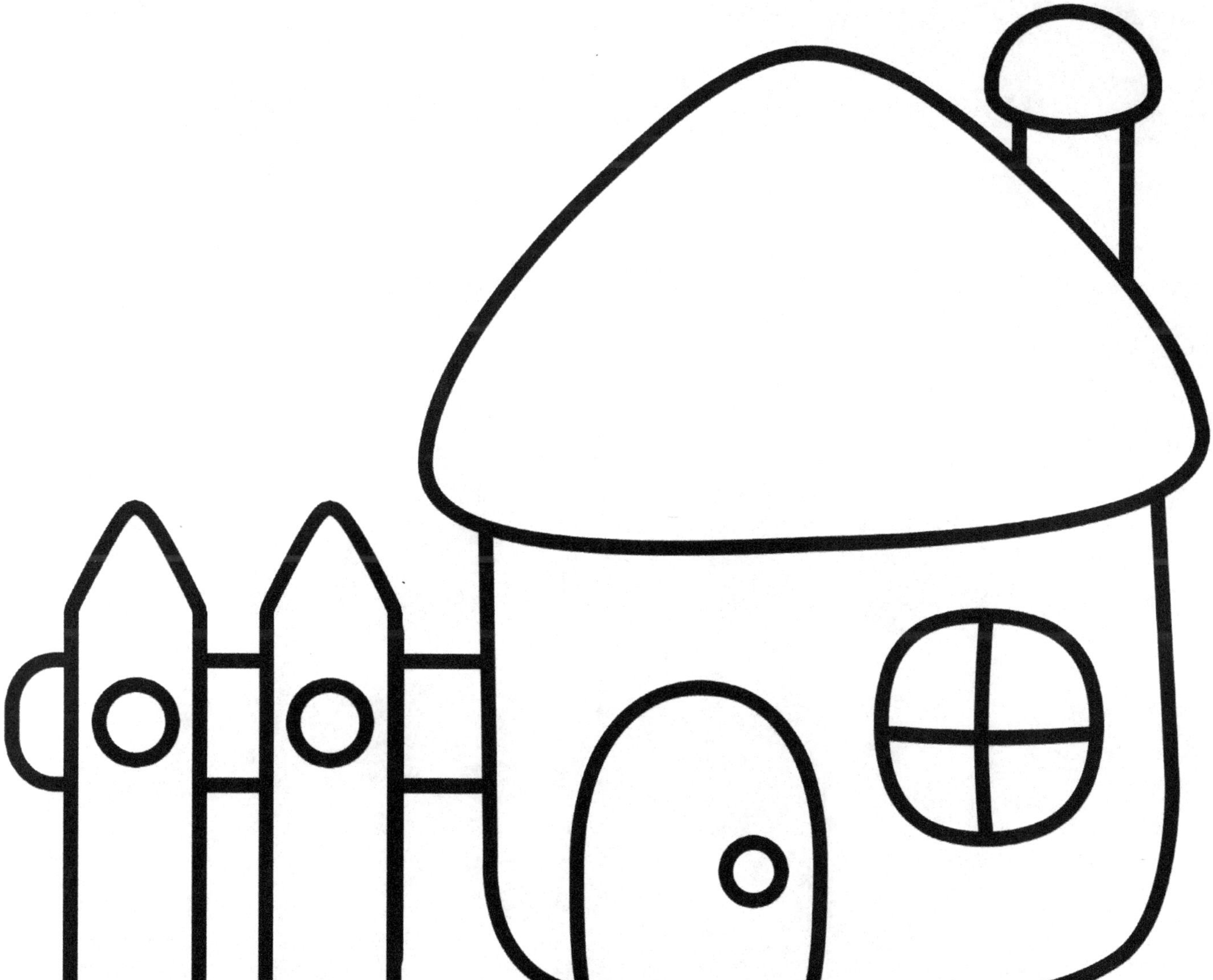

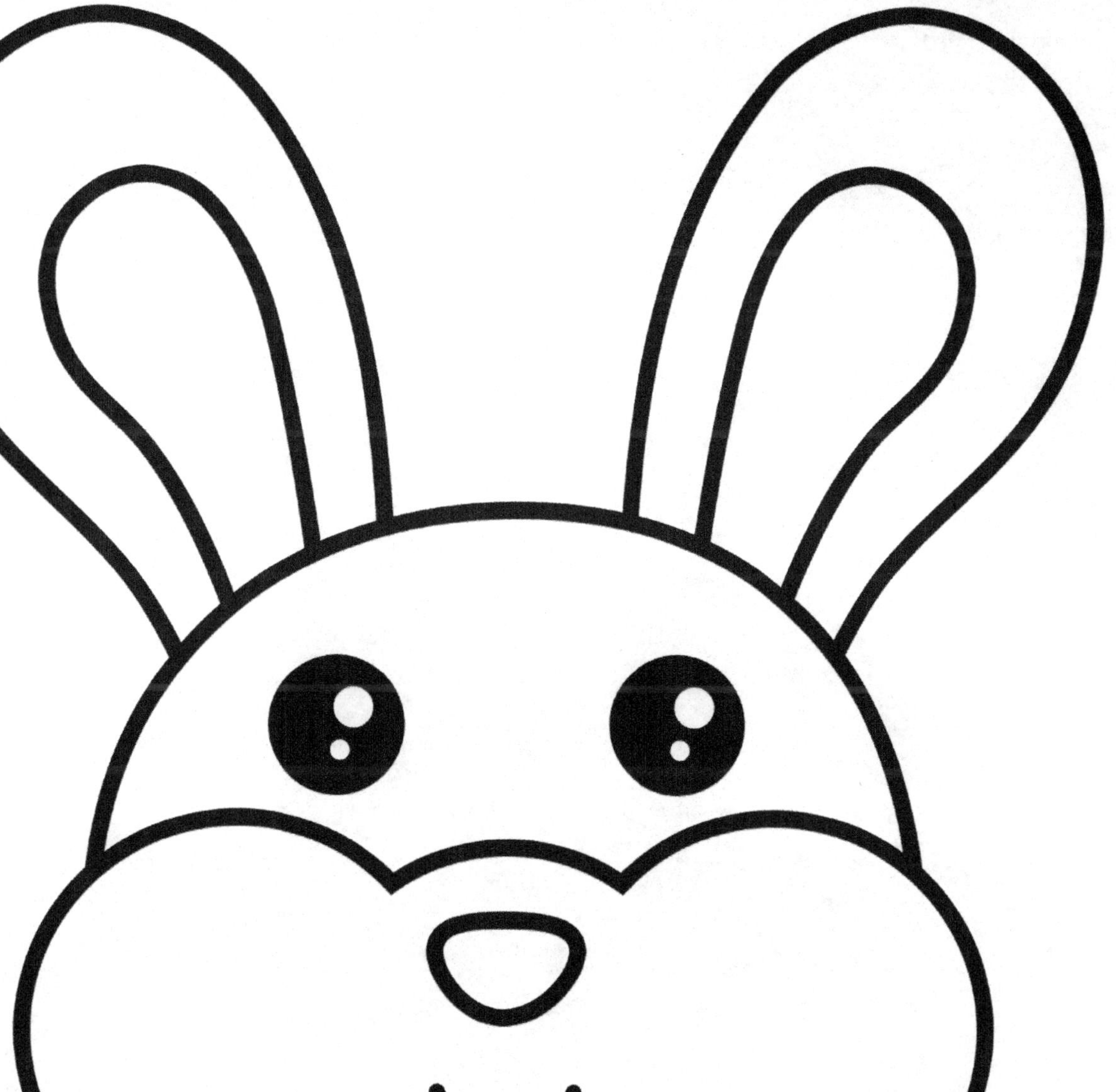

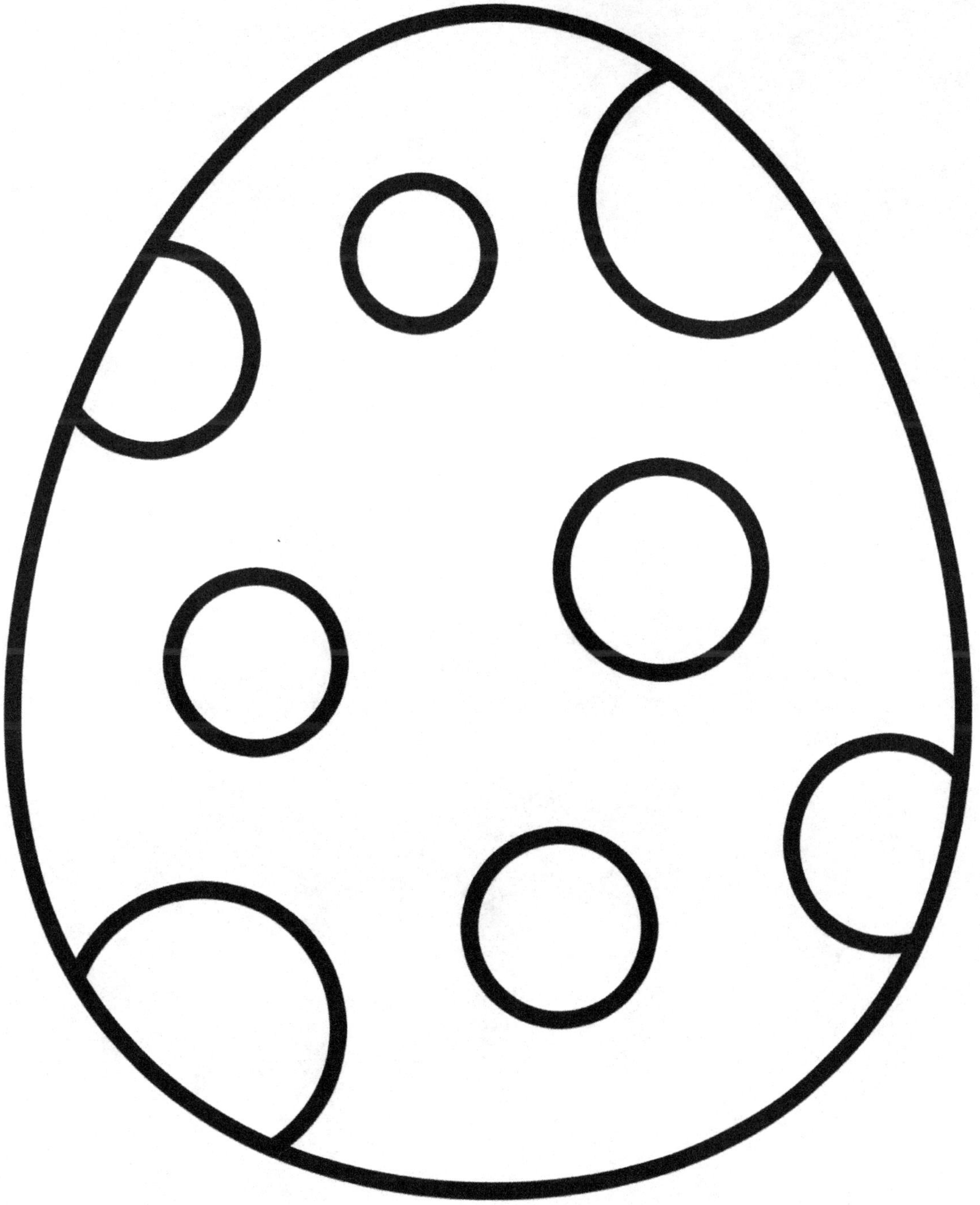

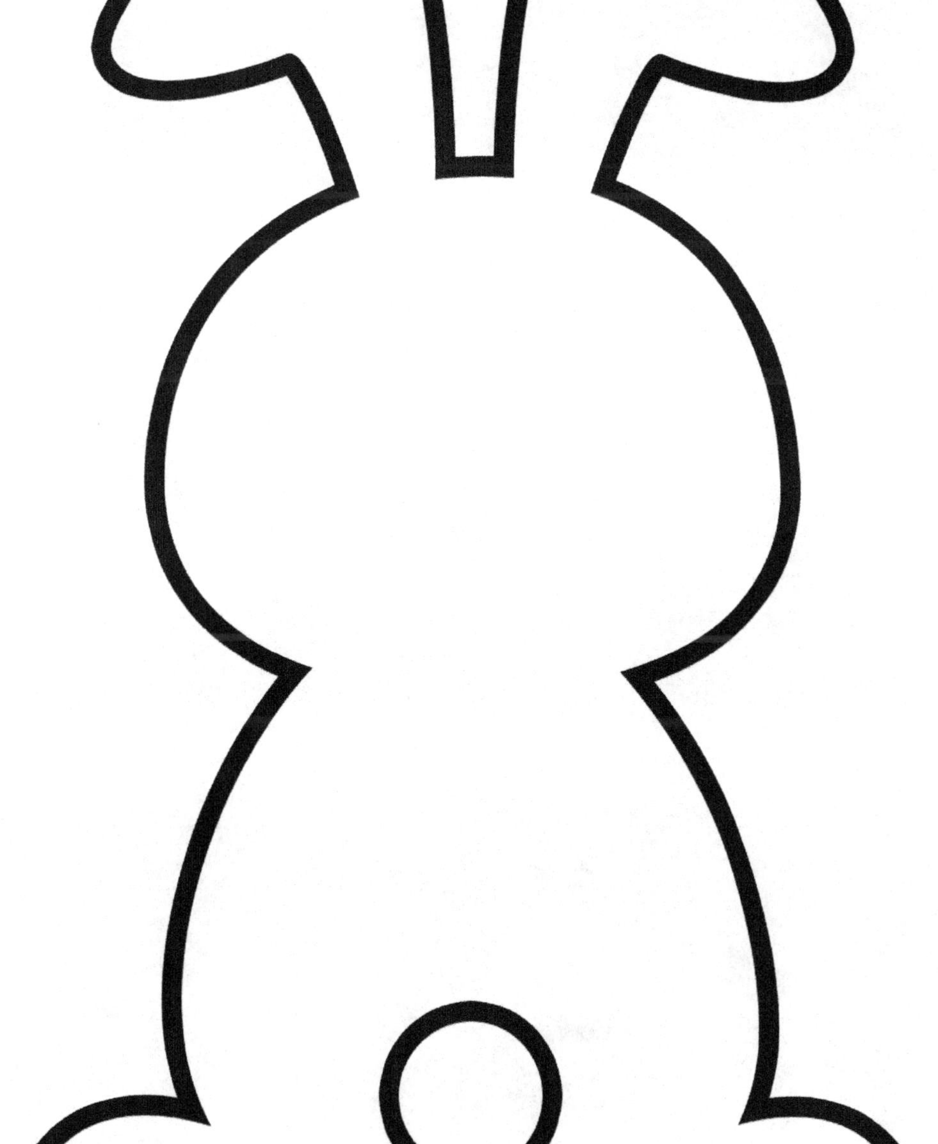

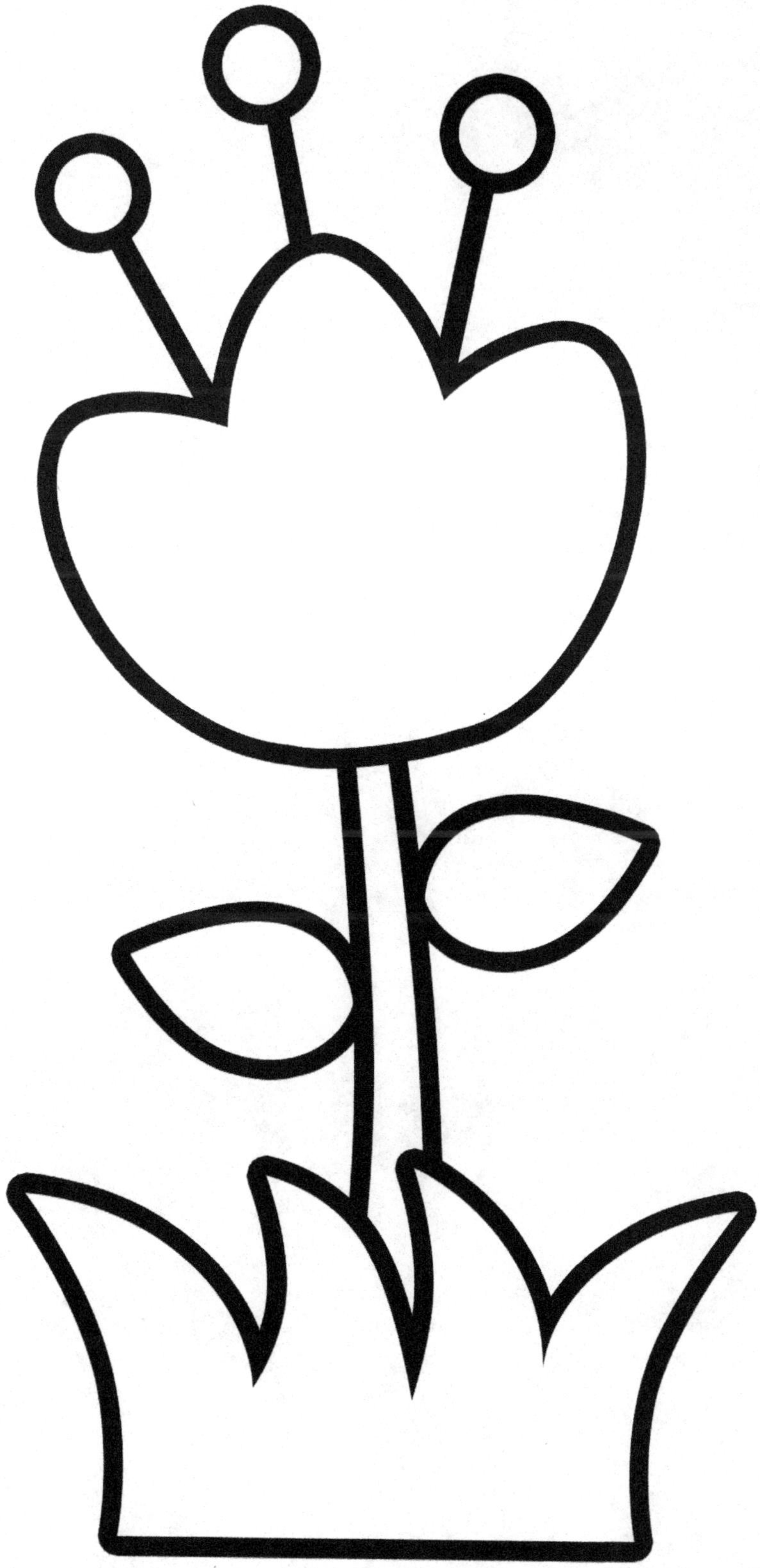

Made in the USA
Monee, IL
06 April 2025